# Snow Mon

CW01086077

...m and Charlotte Guillain

Presented to the children
From
Friends of Ainderby Steeple
School
Autumn 2020

RISING STARS

Finn hated having baths, but his parents always made him have one after he played football.

"Time for a bath and a hair wash!" said Dad as Finn kicked his football boots off after Friday's training session.

Finn groaned. "I had a bath two days ago!" he wailed.

Grumbling, Finn headed into the bathroom.

Later, as he sat in his pyjamas, Mum said, "Let me brush your hair, Finn."

"Ugh, no thanks," said Finn. "I like my hair messy."

Mum sighed and went to answer the phone.

"That was Rav's mum," said Mrs Harrison. "He's going to come with us to the wildlife park tomorrow."

"Yes!" cheered Finn, punching the air.

The next day, Rav and Finn ran to the monkey house.

"I wish I were a monkey," said Finn. "They don't have to worry about baths and hair brushing – they just have fun!"

Rav was holding out some fruit to a baby monkey when snow began to fall and his feet lifted up.

Rav and Finn landed on a snowy mountain. The pine trees were dusted with snow as if they'd been covered in icing sugar.

"Something's moving in that tree," whispered Rav, nudging his friend.

They stared upwards as a little red face emerged from the branches.

"Hello," said a young snow monkey, swinging to the ground. "Welcome to Japan! I'm Manabu – come and meet my troop."

Manabu led them through the deep snow to a group of monkeys laughing and playing.

"You can play with us!" shouted Manabu. He scampered off through the snow while Rav and Finn slithered around laughing. They couldn't keep up with their new monkey friends, but they didn't mind.

"Come up here!" called Manabu, and he bounded up a tall pine tree.

Rav and Finn tried to climb up but got stuck on the bottom branch.

"I told you being a monkey was more fun than being a human," grumbled Finn as they sat gazing upwards.

Rav and Finn jumped at the sound of a loud voice.

"Come on, Manabu!" called a bigger monkey standing at the foot of the tree. "Time to go to the springs!"

"Springs?" said Rav. "That sounds fun. Do you think they're for bouncing around?"

Finn shrugged. "Let's find out!" he said, jumping down.

All the monkeys in the troop were starting to move down the mountain.

"Come now, Manabu!" the monkey called again.

At last, Manabu and his friends appeared through the branches.

"But, Mum, I want to stay here and play," grumbled Manabu.

"Where are the springs?" Finn asked Manabu. "They sound like fun."

"Ugh! No, they're not," groaned Manabu as he slowly followed the troop down the mountainside. "You'll see."

Rav raised his eyebrows at Finn as they trudged along.

They'd walked a long way when Finn spotted a misty haze through the trees.

"Is something on fire?" he gasped.

Manabu laughed. "That's not smoke!" he said. "It's steam from the springs."

Rav and Finn ran to the front of the troop and stared.

The rest of the troop were plunging into a big, steaming pool of water.

"I've heard about this sort of spring!" cried Rav. "They have them in India. It's warm water that's been heated underground. That's amazing!"

"Come on in, Manabu!" called his mother.

"I don't want to," grumbled Manabu. He stayed on the side with Rav and Finn.

They watched as the monkeys in the pool started to pick through each other's fur.

"What are they doing?" asked Finn.

"They're grooming each other," muttered Manabu as he scratched his back.

Manabu's mother looked up at the boys and smiled.

"We groom each other to get rid of dirt and bugs, but it also shows how much we like each other," she said.

Finn glanced at Manabu, who was still scratching.

"Don't you want to join in?" asked Finn. "It looks lovely and warm."

"You could groom me," said Manabu, his eyes lighting up. He called to his mum, "Finn and Rav can groom me here! I don't need to go into the water."

Finn and Rav jumped up.

"I don't want to pick dirt and bugs off him," Rav whispered.

Finn thought quickly. "You know, being a snow monkey is much more fun than being a human," he said.

"Why?" grumbled Manabu. "It's boring just sitting in the springs."

"Not if you find a fun way into the water," replied Finn, pointing at a little slope next to the hot spring.

Rav grinned as he guessed Finn's idea. "We can pat the snow to make a slippery slide!" he said.

Manabu stood at the top of the slope and let out an excited squeal. He threw himself forwards and whizzed down the slope towards the hot spring. With a whoosh, he shot up in the air and landed with a spectacular splash!

"Can we try?" called the other little monkeys. Soon there was a long line of snow monkeys waiting to slide down the slope.

"Thank you!" called Manabu's mother. She snuggled up to Manabu in the water and started to pick through his fur.

Rav watched the young monkeys splashing around. "I wish we had our swimming trunks," he said. He looked up to see snowflakes falling softly from the sky like fluttering white feathers.

"It's time for us to go!" called Finn as his feet lifted up. "Goodbye, Manabu!"

They landed back at the Animal Adventure wildlife park.

"I've been looking for you, boys," Finn's mum said. "Would you like a hot chocolate to help you warm up?"

"Yes please!" said Rav.

"And a nice warm bath when you get home," Finn's mum added.

Only if it's got a slide!

# Talk about the story

Answer the questions:

1 Which country did Rav and Finn travel to?

2 What was the name of the young snow monkey that made friends with the boys?

3 Why did Manabu grumble when his mum told him to come down from the trees?

4 What was the name of the warm water that the monkeys bathed in?

5 What does the word 'grooming' mean? (page 15) Can you think of other words that mean the same or a similar thing?

6 Why did Rav and Finn make a slide?

7 Describe how Manubu felt about the spring at the beginning of the story and how he felt at the end.

8 What animal would you like to see in a snowy country? Why?

Can you retell the story in your own words?